G000147535

My friend Patrick

Learning Unlimited's
'Literacy for Active Citizenship' series

Written by Erica Tate

My friend Patrick
© Learning Unlimited 2018

Published by Learning Unlimited.

No part of this publication may be reproduced in any form or by any means, electronic, mechanical, recording or otherwise, without the prior consent of Learning Unlimited.

Foreword

Learning Unlimited's
'Literacy for Active Citizenship' series

The graded readers in the 'Literacy for Active Citizenship' series are primarily for adults who are settling in the UK, who are speakers of other languages (ESOL) and who are still developing their skills in English and in reading.

The first 20 titles in this series were produced as part of the EU-funded Active Citizenship and English (ACE) project (July 2013 – June 2015), led by Learning Unlimited. The ACE project supported migrant women to develop their skills and confidence in English and to take an active part in everyday life in the UK. We wanted to use the real-life experiences of our learners and volunteers in a writing strand of the project to support adult migrants settling in the UK. These stories, written by learners and volunteers, include funny, personal and less typical aspects of everyday life in the UK.

Additional titles in this series have also been written by learners and volunteers from Learning Unlimited's programmes. These include stories about more serious topics such as crime and health.

We hope you enjoy the 'Literacy for Active Citizenship' series. All the stories have been edited by ESOL specialists at Learning Unlimited. There are two versions of each story – Entry 1 (A1) and Entry 2+ (A2+), each with free downloadable supporting materials:
www.learningunlimited.co/publications/esolreaders

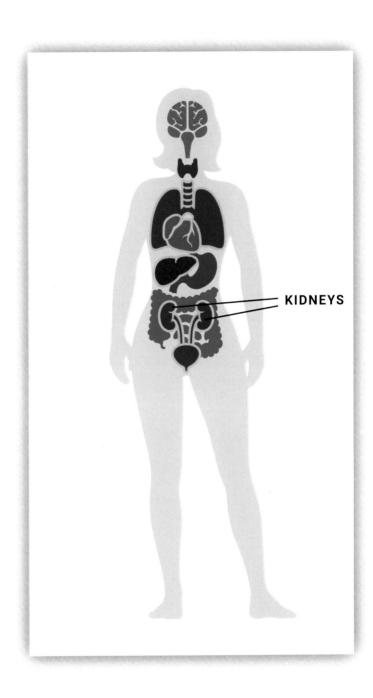

KIDNEYS

My name is Erica.

I have one brother and five sisters.

Four of us have polycystic kidneys.

This is a kidney disease.

We get this disease from our mother.

At 24, doctors told me it was
dangerous to have children.
But I had a beautiful baby boy.
He is now 28 years old.

My mother died of polycystic kidneys.

My brother had two kidney transplants.

One sister had a kidney transplant.

10 years later she is doing well.

Another sister lives in the USA.

She cannot have a kidney transplant.

Her health insurance does not pay for it.

Now she cannot get out of bed.

U - UNITED

S - STATE OF

A - AMERICA

UNITED STATE OF AMERIA

When I am 54 years old, my kidneys
stop working.
Doctors tell me I need a
kidney transplant.
I need a kidney from someone
who has died.

I spend two days a week in hospital.

I have dialysis three times a week.

I am very tired and feel unwell.

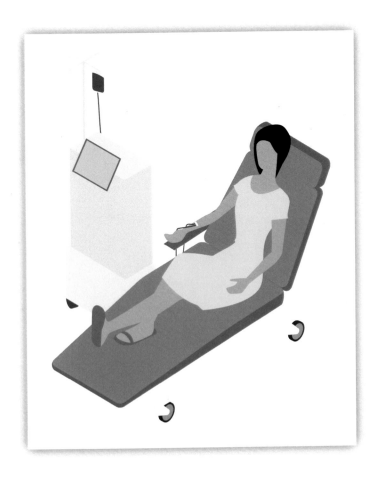

Someone with an organ donor card dies.
A donor card means:

'*Doctors can use my organs after I die
to help other people*'.

I get a new kidney.

I am very lucky.

I feel much better now.

I call my new kidney Patrick.

I have to take a lot of medicine.

I have a lot of hospital appointments.

I hope Patrick works inside me for a long time.

I am very lucky.
Someone's kidney gave me
the gift of life.
If you donate an organ,
you can give someone the
gift of life, too.

To find out more about organ donation, see:
www.organdonation.nhs.uk

Key words

dialysis	cleaning your blood with a machine
donate	to give some money or something to help other people
donor card	a card which tells doctors they can use your organs after you die to help other people
gift	a present from someone
kidney	an organ that cleans the blood
organ	an important part of the body, e.g. heart, lungs, liver
polycystic kidneys	a disease that damages the kidneys
receive	to get something from someone, the opposite of give
transplant	to take an organ from one person and put it into another person

Questions

1. What health problem does Erica have?

2. Why did doctors tell Erica
   not to have children?

3. What happened to Erica's brother
   and sisters?

4. How old is Erica when her kidneys
   stop working?

5. How did Erica feel before her
   kidney transplant?

6. How does Erica feel after her
   kidney transplant?

Talk in pairs:

7. Would you like to give your organs to
   someone when you die?

8. Talk about a time when you, or someone
   close to you, was very ill and got better

Activity 1

Best gifts

Work with a partner. Talk about your best gifts:

• What is the best gift you gave to someone? Why?

• What is the best gift you received from someone? Why?

Tell the group what you find out about best gifts.

For more downloadable activities, visit:
www.learningunlimited.co/publications/esolreaders

Acknowledgements

My friend Patrick was written by Erica Tate. We are grateful to Erica and her family, and the NHS BT image library for being able to include some of their photographs in this book.

My friend Patrick was edited by Karen Dudley, Judy Kirsh, Julia McGerty and Foufou Savitzky at Learning Unlimited.

Images: iStock p.1, 6, Erica Tate, p.1, 2, 10, NHSBT image library p. 5, 7, 8
Cover images: iStock and NHSBT image library

Designed by Daisy Dudley www.daisydudley.com